U.S. EDITION

**Earlybird Kindergarten**

# Mathematics

**2B**

By

## Winnie Tan

Illustrations by

## Paul Yong • Yin Lu

Original edition published under the title Earlybird Preschool Mathematics 2B
© 1998 Federal Publications (S) Pte Ltd
© 2000 Times Media Private Limited
© 2003 Marshall Cavendish International (Singapore) Private Limited

**Marshall Cavendish Education**
A member of Times Publishing Limited
Times Centre, 1 New Industrial Road, Singapore 536196
Customer Service Hotline: (65) 6213 9106
E-mail: fps@sg.marshallcavendish.com
Website: www.marshallcavendish.com/education/sg

Distributed by
SingaporeMath.com Inc
404 Beavercreek Road #225
Oregon City, OR 97045
U.S.A.
Website: http://www.singaporemath.com

First published 2003
Reprinted 2004 (twice)
Second impression 2005
Third impression 2005
Fourth impression 2006
Reprinted 2006

ISBN 981-01-8601-0
ISBN 978-981-01-8601-2

Printed in Singapore by Times Graphics Pte Ltd

**mc Marshall Cavendish**
Education

# CONTENTS

# How many in all?

**Using this page:** Direct the children's attention to the two sets of birds on this page
Ask, "How many birds are sitting on the tree? How many birds are flying towards them?
How many birds are there in all?" To help the children understand this situation clearly, have
them dramatize it. Ask three children to sit on a table like three birds on a tree. Say, "There
are three birds on a tree." Direct two other children to fly like birds towards them and sit
next to them. While they are doing this, say, "Two more birds are joining the three birds.
How many birds are there in all?" Repeat the procedure for combining the two sets of ducks
and combining the two sets of dogs.

# Write the correct numbers in the boxes.

$\boxed{1} + \boxed{2} = \boxed{3}$

$\boxed{\phantom{0}} + \boxed{\phantom{0}} = \boxed{\phantom{0}}$

$\boxed{\phantom{0}} + \boxed{\phantom{0}} = \boxed{\phantom{0}}$

**Before using this page:** Direct three boys and one girl to stand in front of the class. Ask, "How many boys are there? How many girls are there?" Record the responses on the board: $\boxed{3}\ \boxed{1}$. Ask, "How many children are there in all?" Introduce the plus and equal symbols: $\boxed{3+1=4}$. Direct them to read after you, "Three and one are four." Make up other number stories to demonstrate combining two sets together.

**Using this page:** Discuss the example with the children. Direct their attention to the people in the left frame. Ask them to name the number of adults and then the number of children and write the numerals in the appropriate boxes. Then ask them to look at the picture on the right. Ask, "How many persons are there on the bench?" Direct them to record the numeral in the box. Do the same with the second exercise.

# Trace the pictures and write the numbers in the boxes.

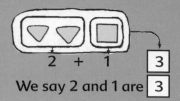

3     +     1     =     [ ]

We say 3 and 1 are [ ]

1     +     2     =     [ ]

We say 1 and 2 are [ ]

**Before using this page:** Divide the children into groups. Ask each group to make up a number song and dramatize it. Write the related number sentence on the board and direct the children to read it after you.

**Using this page:** Ask the children to look at the picture of the penguins. Say, "There are 3 penguins in one set. Trace 1 more penguin to make another set. How many penguins are there altogether?" Direct them to record the answer in the boxes and read the number sentence after you. Do the same with the two sets of lions.

# Write the correct numbers in the boxes.

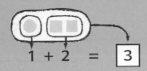

2  +  1  =  ▢

3  +  2  =  ▢

2  +  2  =  ▢

**Before using this page:** Draw on the board: ▱ ▱ Ask a child to write the appropriate numeral below each set. Say, "Now I want to combine these two sets together." Circle them: ▱ ▱ Ask, "How many shapes are there in all?" Write the plus and equal symbols in their correct places and ask a child to complete it: 2 + 3 = _____ .

**Using this page:** Explain the example at the top of the page and direct the children to complete the exercises. Give help where necessary.

# Write the correct numbers in the boxes.

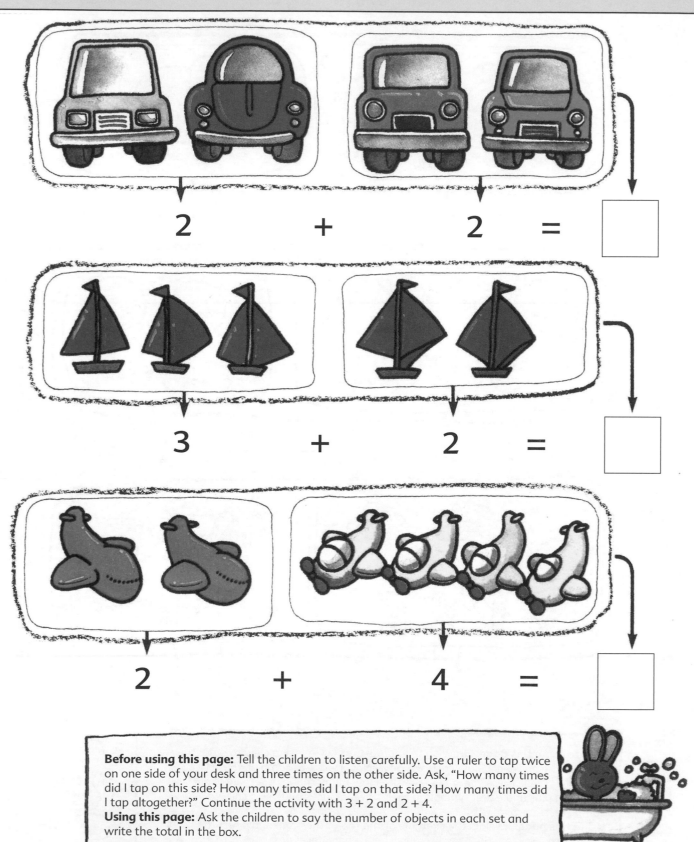

2  +  2  =  ☐

3  +  2  =  ☐

2  +  4  =  ☐

**Before using this page:** Tell the children to listen carefully. Use a ruler to tap twice on one side of your desk and three times on the other side. Ask, "How many times did I tap on this side? How many times did I tap on that side? How many times did I tap altogether?" Continue the activity with 3 + 2 and 2 + 4.
**Using this page:** Ask the children to say the number of objects in each set and write the total in the box.

# Write the correct numbers in the boxes.

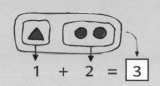

1 + 2 = 3

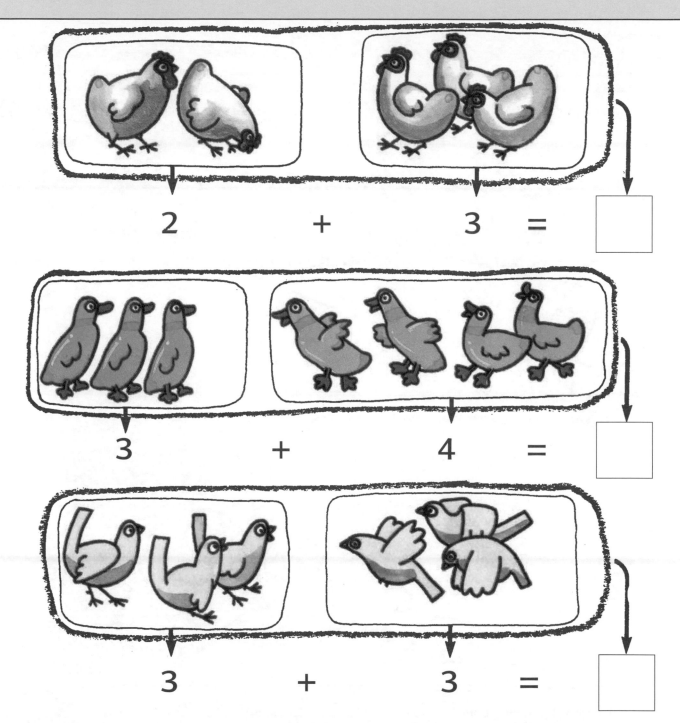

2 + 3 = ☐

3 + 4 = ☐

3 + 3 = ☐

**Before using this page:** Hold a mini competition. Have the children stand in two columns. Call out a sum, e.g. 2 + 1. The first child from each column then runs to the board and writes the answer. Award points for correct answers. Use different numbers with a sum of 10 or less.

**Using this page:** Ask the children to say the number of objects in each set and write the total in the box.

**Using this page:** Recite the nursery rhyme, *Little Bo Peep* to the children and ask one child to recite it. Then talk about the picture with the children. Lead them to see that Bo Peep has two bows in her hair and one bow on her crook (stick). Ask, "How many bows are there altogether?" Next, point out the flowers on Bo Peep's dress. Say, "There are three colored flowers and two white flowers on her dress. How many flowers are there altogether?" Tell the children this number story. Use a felt board if necessary: "Little Bo Peep is very sad. In the morning she counted her sheep. She had five white sheep and four black ones. How many sheep did she have altogether? In the evening eight sheep came home. There were five white ones. How many black ones were there? Who can tell how many sheep were missing?"

# Trace the pictures and write the numbers in the blanks.

 $\underline{4} + \underline{2} = 6$

_____ + _____ = 6

_____ + _____ = 6

_____ + _____ = 6

_____ + _____ = 6

_____ + _____ = 6

**Before using this page:** String 6 spools or clothes-pins. Ask a child to separate them into two parts, e.g. 1 and 5. Have him record on the board 1 + 5 = 6. Combine them again and ask another child to separate them into two parts. Proceed in the same manner drawing the children's attention to the different combinations of numbers which add up to 6.

**Using this page:** Guide the children to identify and count the number of vases in the first row. Then have them trace 1 vase and write 1 in the first blank. Then trace 5 vases in another color in the first row and write 5 in the second blank. Proceed in the same way for the remaining exercises.

# Color and write the numbers in the blanks.

$2+3=5$
$2+2+1=5$

## Green  Red

___ + ___ = 7

___ + ___ = 7

___ + ___ = 7

___ + ___ = 7

## Blue  Red   Green

___ + ___ + ___ = 7

___ + ___ + ___ = 7

___ + ___ + ___ = 7

___ + ___ + ___ = 7

**Before using this page:** Display seven objects on a demonstration table. Ask one child to separate this set into two subsets. Write the combination on the board, e.g. 3 + 4 = 7. Combine the seven objects again and ask another child to separate them into two subsets. Proceed in the same way drawing the children's attention to the different combinations of numbers which add up to seven.

**Using this page:** Ask the children to count and say how many beads there are in each row (7). Direct them to color one bead green and record 1 in the first blank, and then color the remaining six beads red and write 6 in the second blank. Proceed in the same way with two green beads in the second row, three in the third row, etc. Proceed similarly with the second exercise.

12

# Color and write the numbers in the blanks.

Red   Blue

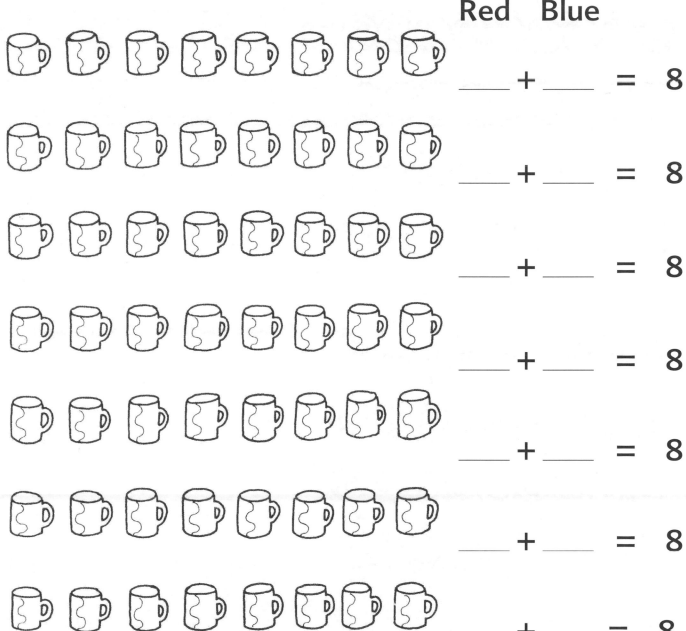

___ + ___ = 8

___ + ___ = 8

___ + ___ = 8

___ + ___ = 8

___ + ___ = 8

___ + ___ = 8

___ + ___ = 8

**Before using this page:** Ask eight children to stand in the one straight row in front of the class. Direct the first child to take one big step sideways. Ask the class to give the number combination: 1 + 7 = 8. Direct the second child to move to the first child and ask the class to give the number combination: 2 + 6 = 8, and so on.
**Using this page:** Ask the children to count and tell how many mugs there are in each row. Direct them to color 1 mug red and write 1 in the first blank. Direct them to color the remaining 7 mugs blue and write 7 in the second blank. Continue in the same manner until they know what to do.

# Color and write the numbers in the blanks.

**Blue   Red**

___ + ___ = 9

___ + ___ = 9

___ + ___ = 9

___ + ___ = 9

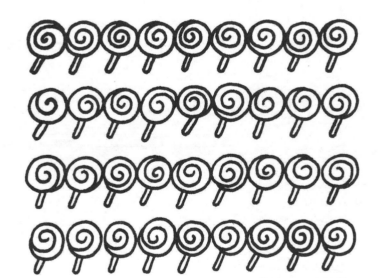

**Red   Blue   Green**

___ + ___ + ___ = 9

___ + ___ + ___ = 9

___ + ___ + ___ = 9

___ + ___ + ___ = 9

**Before using this page:** Draw a circle on the board. Write the numeral 9 in the center and the numerals 1 to 8 all round the circle in random order. Give each child nine counters. Point to the numeral 4. Ask the children to use their nine counters to find out what number and four add up to nine. Ask one child to write the number sentence on the board like this: 4 + 5 = 9. If he gets the answer right, he points to one of the numerals outside the circle and nominates another child to write the number sentence on the board and so the game goes on.
**Using this page:** Direct the children to complete the exercises in the same way as on the previous page.

14

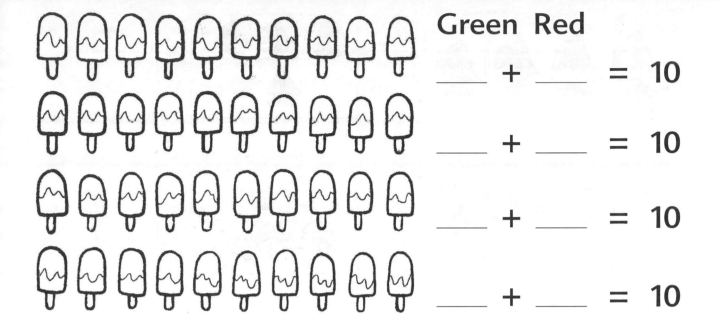

## Green  Red

___ + ___ = 10

___ + ___ = 10

___ + ___ = 10

___ + ___ = 10

## Green  Red  Blue

___ + ___ + ___ = 10

___ + ___ + ___ = 10

___ + ___ + ___ = 10

___ + ___ + ___ = 10

**Using this page:** The exercises on this page are similar to those on the two previous pages, so the children should be able to work on their own. However, give individual help where necessary.

# Add.

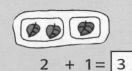 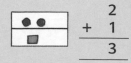

2 + 1 = 3

---

3 + 1 =

3
+ 1
___

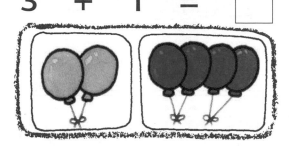

2 + 4 =

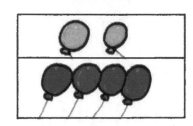

2
+ 4
___

2 + 1 =

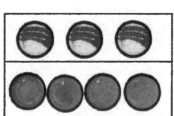

2
+ 1
___

3 + 4 =

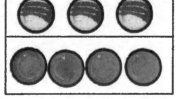

3
+ 4
___

**Before using this page:** Attach five clothes-pins along one side of a rectangular card to show 3 + 2. Hold the card in a horizontal position and ask, "What is 3 + 2?" Write the answer like this:  3 + 2 = 5.

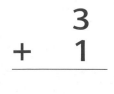

3 + 2 = 5

Next, turn the card to a vertical position and record the sum like this: Tell the children that this is another way of writing 3 + 2 and we read it in the same way: "Three and two make five." Illustrate various examples using the card and clothes-pins.

3
+ 2
___
5

**Using this page:** Ask the children to tell the number of boats in each set and in the combined set. Draw their attention to the same sum written in both the horizontal and vertical forms. Ask them to read both sums in the same way: "Three and one make four." Do the exercise orally with them and direct them to work this page from left to right.

# Add.

$$\begin{array}{r} 1 \\ + \ 2 \\ \hline 3 \end{array}$$

1 + 2 = 3

$$\begin{array}{r} 3 \\ + \ 3 \\ \hline \end{array}$$

$$\begin{array}{r} 2 \\ + \ 5 \\ \hline \end{array}$$

$$\begin{array}{r} 4 \\ + \ 4 \\ \hline \end{array}$$

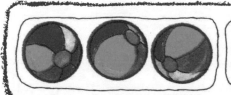

$$\begin{array}{r} 4 \\ + \ 2 \\ \hline \end{array}$$

3 + 2 = ☐

3 + 1 = ☐

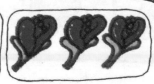

3 + 3 = ☐

4 + 1 = ☐

**Before using this page:** Have available ten clothes-pins and a rectangular card. Clip the clothes-pins along the top of the card to show 3 + 5. Ask a child to write the addition sum on the board while the class supplies the answer: **3 + 5 = 8** Turn the card to a vertical position and ask another child to write the same addition sum in the vertical form while the class supplies the answer:

$$\begin{array}{r} 3 \\ + \ 5 \\ \hline 8 \end{array}$$

Repeat with various combinations.

**Using this page:** Direct the children to complete this page by finding the sum. Give individual help where necessary.

17

# Write the correct numbers in the boxes.

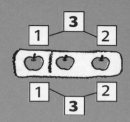

**Before using this page:** Draw six circles on the board. Ask, "How many circles are there?" Write 6 above the circles. Say, "We can separate them into two sets. Draw a line to form a set of 2 and a set of 4. Ask one child to write the numeral below each set. Ask, "How many circles are there altogether?" Lead them to realize that 6 is 2 and 4, or that 2 and 4 add up to 6.

**Using this page:** Ask the children to look at the elephants. Ask, How many elephants are there altogether?" Have them point to the numeral 3. Ask, "How many are girl elephants? How many are boy elephants?" Direct the children to record the numerals above each set. Ask, " What is 2 and 1?" Direct the children to write the numeral 3 in the box below the sets. Have them say after you, "Three is two and one. Two and one add up to three." Do the same with the second exercise.

# Write the correct numbers in the boxes.

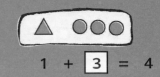
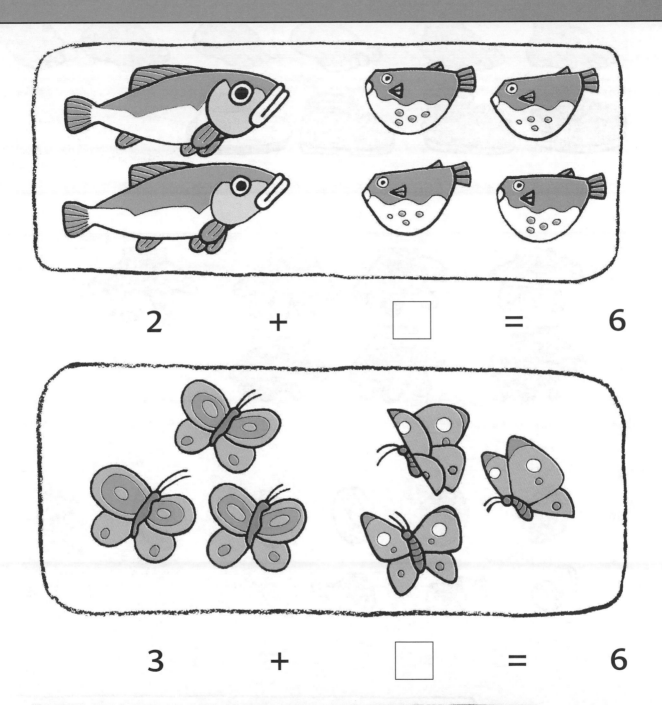

2     +     ☐     =     6

3     +     ☐     =     6

**Before using this page:** Give each child five counters. Say, "Put five counters on your table. Separate them into two sets with your pencil so that there are two counters in the first set. How many are there in the second set? Two and what number add up to five?" Write: 2 + 3 = 5. Repeat the activity using various sets, e.g. 2 + ☐ = 4, 1 + ☐ = 5.
**Using this page:** Ask the children to look at the fish and say the number of fish in each set and how many fish there are altogether. Direct them to fill in the missing number. In the second exercise, ask the children to draw a line between the two sets of butterflies, say the numbers in each set and the total, and fill in the missing number.

# Trace the pictures and fill in the missing numbers.

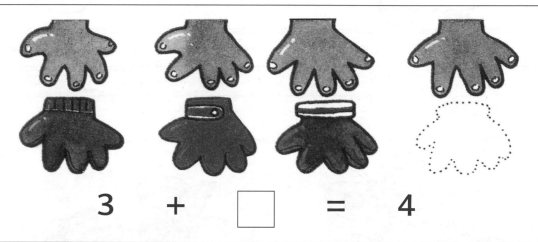

4 + ☐ = 6

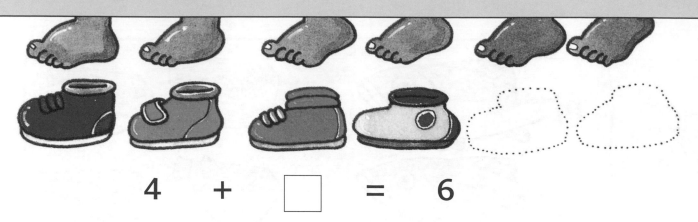

3 + ☐ = 4

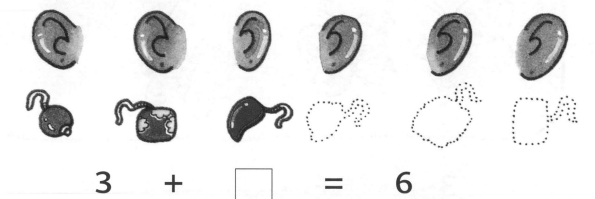

3 + ☐ = 6

**Before using this page:** Call four children to the front of the class. Ask them to take off their shoes and sit in a row facing the other children. Take away three shoes. Ask, "How many feet are there?" (8) Count the number of feet with the children. Then say, "But there are only five shoes." Write 5 + ☐ = 8 on the board. Ask, "How many more shoes do they need?" Ask one child to record the answer on the board.

**Using this page:** Direct the children to draw lines linking each shoe to a foot, each glove to a hand, etc. Ask, "Is there a shoe for each foot? How many feet need shoes?" Have them trace the picture of the shoes and write the number in the box. Proceed in the same way for the second exercise.

# Trace the pictures and fill in the missing numbers.

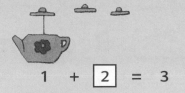

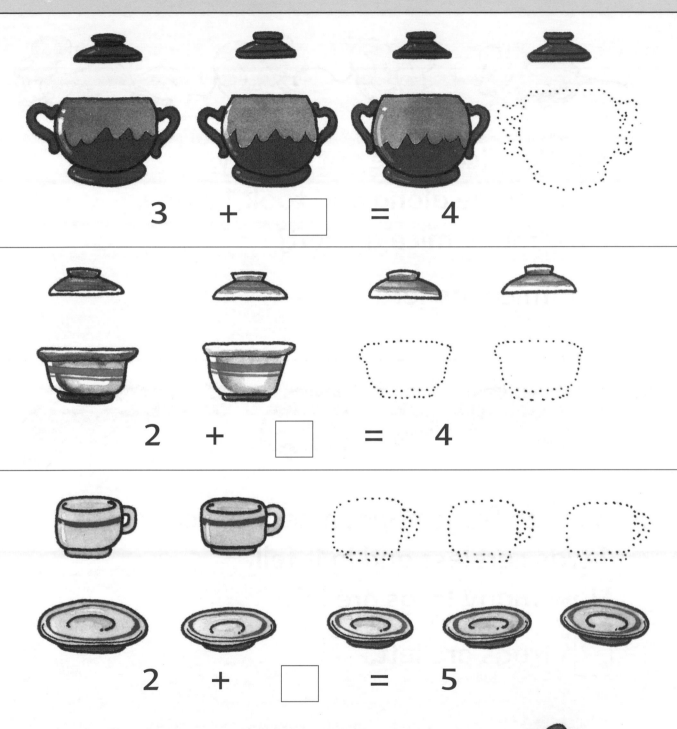

3 + ☐ = 4

2 + ☐ = 4

2 + ☐ = 5

**Before using this page:** Ask five children to stand in a row in front of the class. Put three balls in front of them. Ask, "How many children are there? How many balls are there? Is there a ball for each child? How many more balls do they need? Three and what number make five?" Record the answer on the board like this: 3 + 2 = 5.

**Using this page:** Direct the children to look at the first exercise. Ask, "How many covers are there? (4) But there are only 3 pots. How many more pots do we need to make 4?" Direct them to trace the picture of the pot and record 1 in the box. Let them complete the remaining exercises on their own. Give individual help to those who need it.

# Read and do.

4 little mice came out to play,
A cat came along and took 1 away.
How many mice are left?

☐ mice are left.

3 green frogs hopped near a well,
1 was careless and in it fell.
How many frogs are left?

☐ frogs are left.

**Using this page:** Read the first rhyme to the children and ask them to dramatize it. Ask, "How many mice were there at first? How many mice did the cat take away? How many mice were left?" Direct them to write the answer in the box. Introduce the second rhyme in the same manner. Draw a circle on the floor to represent the well.

# Count back.

## Put your finger on 5. Count back 2. What do you get?

| 1 | 2 | 3 | 4 | 5 | 6 | 7 | 8 | 9 | 10 |

5 take away 2 = _____

## Put your finger on 4. Count back 1. What do you get?

| 1 | 2 | 3 | 4 | 5 | 6 | 7 | 8 | 9 | 10 |

4 take away 1 = _____

## Put your finger on 5. Count back 3. What do you get?

| 1 | 2 | 3 | 4 | 5 | 6 | 7 | 8 | 9 | 10 |

5 take away 3 = _____

## Put your finger on 6. Count back 4. What do you get?

| 1 | 2 | 3 | 4 | 5 | 6 | 7 | 8 | 9 | 10 |

6 take away 4 = _____

**Before using this page:** Draw a number line 1 to 10 on the floor and have a child stand behind each numeral. Direct the 10 children to return to their seats one at a time while the rest of the children read the numerals on the number line: 10, 9, 8 ...
For counting backwards in twos, direct the children to go back to their seats two at a time. Direct the rest of the children to say 10, 8, 6 ...
**Using this page:** Draw the children's attention to the first number strip and help them with the instruction until they are confident to do the exercise. Have them record the answer and read it after you: "Five take away two leaves three." Proceed in the same way with the remaining exercises.

# Write the correct number in the boxes.

4 take away 2 = 2

There are 3 . Cross out 1.

3 take away 1 = ☐

There are 5 ♥. Cross out 3.

5 take away 3 = ☐

There are 4 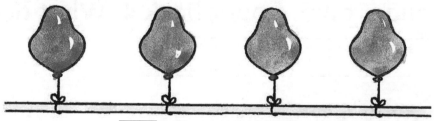. Cross out 4.

4 take away 4 = ☐

**Before using this page:** Label five paper cups 1 to 5 and place them in order on your table. Ask the children to read the numerals. Remove 2 cups from the right. Ask the children to read the numerals on the remaining cups. Ask, "What is 5 take away 2". Repeat the activity with various numbers.

**Using this page:** Discuss the example with the children. Then ask them to count the balloons in the first row. Direct them to cross out 1 balloon from the right. Ask, "How many balloons are left?" What is 3 take away 1? Write your answer in the box." Continue with the rest of the exercises in the same manner.

# Write the correct numbers in the boxes.

How many 🏮 are there? ☐ Cross out 2.

6 take away 2 = ☐

How many 🏮 are there? ☐ Cross out 4.

7 take away 4 = ☐

How many 🏮 are there? ☐ Cross out 4.

6 take away 4 = ☐

**Using this page:** Discuss the example with the children. Then ask, "How many lanterns are there in the first row? Have them record 6 in the box. Direct them to cross out 2 lanterns from the right. Ask, "How many lanterns are left? What is 6 take away 4? Write your answer in the box". Let them try to complete the rest of the exercises on their own.

# Write the correct numbers in the boxes.

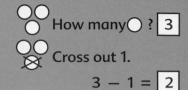

How many ? □
Cross out 6.

8 − 6 = □

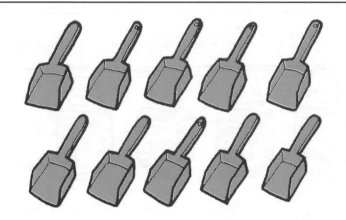

How many ? □
Cross out 4.

10 − 4 = □

How many ? □
Cross out 4.

8 − 4 = □

**Before using this page:** Draw a set of 4 objects on the board. Ask a child to cross out 3 of them. Help them to suggest a subtraction sentence illustrated by the action. Then write it on the board: 4 − 3 = 1. Continue to develop this concept with various sets within 10.

**Using this page:** Draw the children's attention to the set of buckets. Ask, "How many buckets are there?" Ask them to write the numeral 8 in the first box. Instruct them to cross out 6 buckets. Ask, "How many buckets are left?" Direct them to write the numeral 2 in the answer box and have them read the number sentence after you: "Eight take away six leaves two." Continue the remaining exercises in the same manner.

## Write the correct numbers in the boxes.

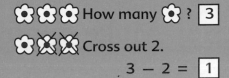

How many 🐔 ? ☐
Cross out 2.

7 − 2 = ☐

How many 🦆 ? ☐
Cross out 4.

7 − 4 = ☐

How many 🐦 ? ☐
Cross out 1.

5 − 1 = ☐

How many 🐦 ? ☐
Cross out 5.

6 − 5 = ☐

**Using this page:** Direct the children's attention to the set of chickens in the first frame. Ask, "How many chickens are there?" Help them to realize that the numeral 7 in the number sentence represents the set of 7 chickens. Instruct them to cross out 2 chickens and call their attention to the numeral 2. Ask, "How many chickens are left?" They write the numeral 5 in the answer box. For the second exercise, ask the children to read the instructions with you and let them do the exercise orally. Allow them to try to do the remaining exercise by themselves. Give attention to those who need help.

# Make a moving picture card.

**1. You need :**

envelope

white card

scissors

crayons

**2. Cut.**

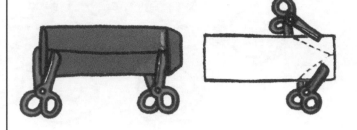

**3. Draw a hungry rabbit on the envelope.**

**4. Draw 4 carrots on the card.**

**5. Slide the card into the envelope and tell a story.**

There are 4 carrots.

The rabbit eats 3 carrots.
There is 1 carrot left.

$4 - 3 = \boxed{1}$

## Use your moving picture card to do these sums.

$4 - 1 = \boxed{\phantom{0}}$    $4 - 2 = \boxed{\phantom{0}}$

$4 - 3 = \boxed{\phantom{0}}$    $4 - 4 = \boxed{\phantom{0}}$

**Activity and using this page:** Each child needs a long white envelope and a plain card to fit it. Help the children to make a moving picture apparatus by following step by step the instructions on this page. When they have made their apparatus, teach them how to use it. It is explained in the last picture. Direct them to use it to complete the exercise.

# Write the correct numbers in the boxes.

$3 - \boxed{1} = \boxed{2}$

$8 - \boxed{\phantom{0}} = \boxed{\phantom{0}}$

$9 - \boxed{\phantom{0}} = \boxed{\phantom{0}}$

$7 - \boxed{\phantom{0}} = \boxed{\phantom{0}}$

**Before using this page:** Write the numeral 5 on the board. Direct the children to put 5 objects on their desks. Ask them to use their ruler to divide the objects into a set of 2 and another set. Ask, "How many objects are there in the smaller set? How many objects are there in the greater set? Which set do you want to take away?" If the response is the greater set of 3, write 5 − 3 on the board. Ask, "Which set is left?" Complete the equation on the board: 5 − 3 = 2. Using the same procedure to explain 5 − 2 = 3.

**Using this page:** Draw the children's attention to the bowls in the first exercise. Help them to decide which set they wish to take away. Ask them to circle the set and write its numeral in the first box. Ask, "How many bowls are there in the remaining set?" Direct them to write the numeral in the answer box and have them read the number sentence. Continue the remaining exercises in the same manner.

# Write the correct numbers in the boxes.

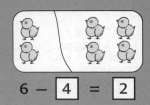

6 − 4 = 2

8 − ☐ = ☐

5 − ☐ = ☐

7 − ☐ = ☐

**Using this page:** Ask, "How many rabbits are there altogether? They are separated into two sets. How many rabbits are there in the first set? How many rabbits are there in the second set? Which set do you want to take away?" Direct them to write the numeral in the first box. Ask, "How many rabbits are there in the remaining set?" Direct them to write the number in the answer box.

# Write the correct numbers in the boxes.

6 − 2 = ☐          7 − 3 = ☐

6 − 3 = ☐          4 − 2 = ☐

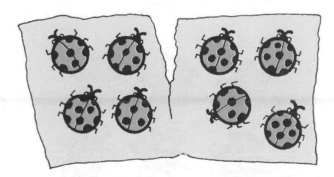 

8 − 4 = ☐          8 − 5 = ☐

**Activity:** Place a set of 8 toy bowling pins or plastic bottles on the floor. Instruct a child to bowl a tennis ball and count how many bowling pins/plastic bottles he can knock down at one time. Ask him to write the related number sentence on the board. Name another child to play the game. You may vary the number of bowling pins/plastic bottles each time.

**Using this page:** Direct the children's attention to the first picture. Ask, "How many ducks are there altogether? If you take away 2 ducks, how many ducks are left?" Instruct them to write 4 in the box. You may want to do two more exercises with them and let them complete the rest by themselves.

# Cross out the number and do the sums.

$$4$$
$$-1$$
$$\overline{\phantom{-}3}$$

$$4 - 1 = \boxed{3}$$

## Cross out 5.

$$8$$
$$-5$$
$$\overline{\phantom{-}}$$

$$8 - 5 = \boxed{\phantom{0}}$$

## Cross out 3.

$$7$$
$$-3$$
$$\overline{\phantom{-}}$$

$$7 - 3 = \boxed{\phantom{0}}$$

## Cross out 6.

$$10$$
$$-\phantom{0}6$$
$$\overline{\phantom{-}}$$

$$10 - 6 = \boxed{\phantom{0}}$$

## Cross out 3.

$$9$$
$$-3$$
$$\overline{\phantom{-}}$$

$$9 - 3 = \boxed{\phantom{0}}$$

## Cross out 5.

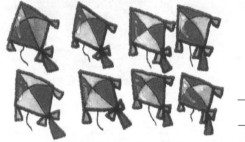

$$8$$
$$-5$$
$$\overline{\phantom{-}}$$

$$8 - 5 = \boxed{\phantom{0}}$$

## Cross out 2.

$$6$$
$$-2$$
$$\overline{\phantom{-}}$$

$$6 - 2 = \boxed{\phantom{0}}$$

**Before using this page:** Hold up a strip of paper on which is drawn 5 circles. Tell the class we want to take away 2 circles. Cross out 2 circles and write the related number sentence on the board.

$$5 - 2 = 3$$

Turn the strip clockwise and hold it up vertically. Lead the children to see that this is merely another way to write the subtraction and we read it in exactly the same way: "Five take away two leaves three."

$$5$$
$$-2$$
$$\overline{\phantom{-}3}$$

**Using this page:** Discuss the example with the children and work the exercises with them until they are confident of doing the exercises by themselves.

# Cross out the number and do the sums.

$4 - 2 = \boxed{2}$

## Cross out 4.

$$\begin{array}{r} 6 \\ -\ 4 \\ \hline \\ \hline \end{array}$$

$6 - 4 = \square$

## Cross out 3.

$$\begin{array}{r} 8 \\ -\ 3 \\ \hline \\ \hline \end{array}$$

$8 - 3 = \square$

## Cross out 5.

$$\begin{array}{r} 9 \\ -\ 5 \\ \hline \\ \hline \end{array}$$

$9 - 5 = \square$

## Cross out 6.

$$\begin{array}{r} 9 \\ -\ 6 \\ \hline \\ \hline \end{array}$$

$9 - 6 = \square$

## Cross out 8.

$$\begin{array}{r} 8 \\ -\ 8 \\ \hline \\ \hline \end{array}$$

$8 - 8 = \square$

## Cross out 2.

$$\begin{array}{r} 5 \\ -\ 2 \\ \hline \\ \hline \end{array}$$

$5 - 2 = \square$

**Using this page:** The exercises on this page are the same as the ones on the previous page except the numbers are different. The children should be able to do this page independently. However, give individual help to those who need it.

# Cross out the number and do the sums.

$$5 - 2 = \boxed{3}$$

## Cross out 7.

$$10 - 7 = \square$$

## Cross out 4.

$$9 - 4 = \square$$

## Cross out 3.

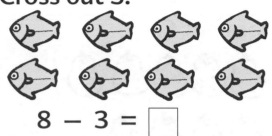

$$8 - 3 = \square$$

## Cross out 5.

$$7 - 5 = \square$$

## Cross out 2.

$$\begin{array}{r} 8 \\ - \ 2 \\ \hline \end{array}$$

## Cross out 3.

$$\begin{array}{r} 6 \\ - \ 3 \\ \hline \end{array}$$

## Cross out 4.

$$\begin{array}{r} 7 \\ - \ 4 \\ \hline \end{array}$$

## Cross out 6.

$$\begin{array}{r} 10 \\ - \ 6 \\ \hline \end{array}$$

**Using this page:** Direct the children to look at the set of vases in the first frame. Ask, "How many vases are there in all?" When the children have responded 10, draw their attention to the numeral 10 in the number sentence. Point out to them the subtraction symbol and the numeral 7. Ask, "How many vases must you cross out?" Make them do it. Ask, "How many vases are left?" Ask them to record the answer in the blank. Allow them the opportunity to complete the remaining exercises by themselves. Give help to those who need it.

# Fill in the missing numbers.

3 take away ☐1 leaves ☐2

3 − ☐1 = ☐2

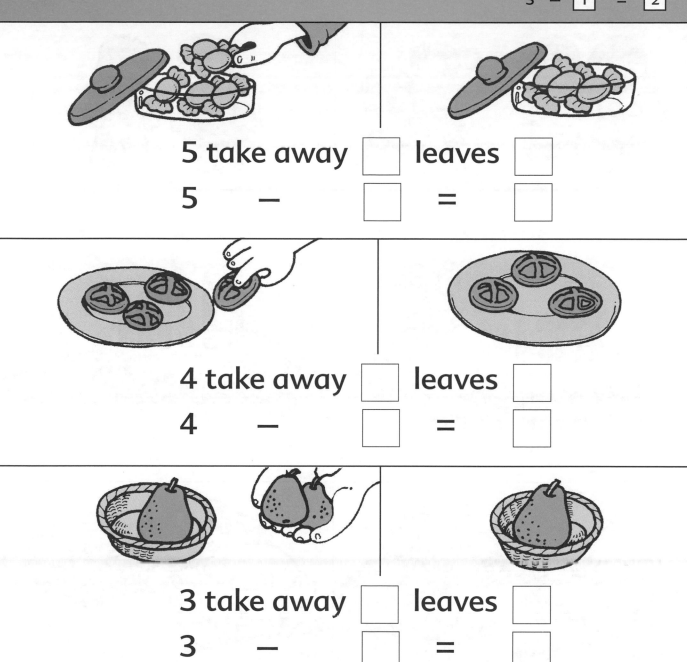

5 take away ☐ leaves ☐

5 − ☐ = ☐

4 take away ☐ leaves ☐

4 − ☐ = ☐

3 take away ☐ leaves ☐

3 − ☐ = ☐

**Before using this page:** Ask the children to put 5 counters on their tables. Ask, "How many objects are there on your table?" Direct them to take away 3 objects. Ask, "How many objects have you taken away? How many objects are left?" Build the number sentence on the board as you ask them questions. Ask them to read the number sentence after you: "Five take away three leaves two." Repeat the activity with various numbers of counters within 5.

**Using this page:** Draw the children's attention to the hand taking out candies from the jar in the first picture. Ask, "Do you see 5 candies?" Ask a child to describe what is happening to the candies. Ask the children to record the numerals in the boxes. Have them read the number sentences after you. Do the remaining exercises with them.

# Fill in the missing numbers.

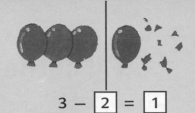

$$4 - \boxed{\phantom{0}} = \boxed{\phantom{0}}$$

$$6 - \boxed{\phantom{0}} = \boxed{\phantom{0}}$$

$$4 - \boxed{\phantom{0}} = \boxed{\phantom{0}}$$

**Activity and using this page:** Talk about the first set of pictures and have the children dramatize it. Ask a volunteer to write the number sentence on the board. Have them look at the first set of pictures on this page again. Guide them to fill in the correct numerals in the boxes. Direct the children's attention to the set of candles in the first picture of the second row. Ask, "How many candles are there altogether?" Lead them to see that the numeral 6 below the picture stands for the 6 candles. Ask, "How many candles have been blown out?" Direct them to write the numeral 4 in the box. Ask, "How many candles are still lighted?" Direct them to write the numeral 2 in the answer box. Proceed with the last exercise in the same manner.

36

# Fill in the missing numbers.

$$3 - \boxed{2} = \boxed{1}$$

$$6 - \boxed{\phantom{0}} = \boxed{\phantom{0}}$$

$$6 - \boxed{\phantom{0}} = \boxed{\phantom{0}}$$

$$5 - \boxed{\phantom{0}} = \boxed{\phantom{0}}$$

**Using this page:** Remind the children that they have done this type of picture stories in their previous lesson. Ask them to study each set of pictures and describe the situation. Help them by asking questions so that they are able to supply the missing numerals in the boxes.

# Trace the pictures. Then fill in the missing numbers.

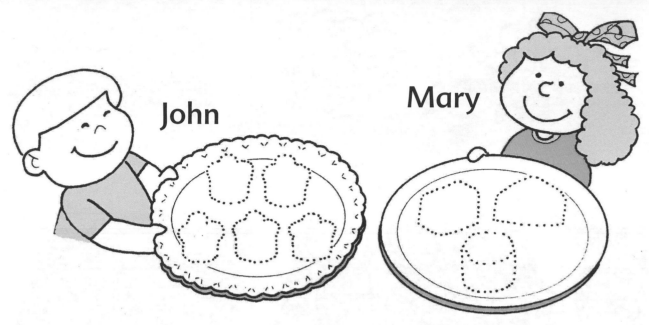

John has _____ more cakes than Mary.

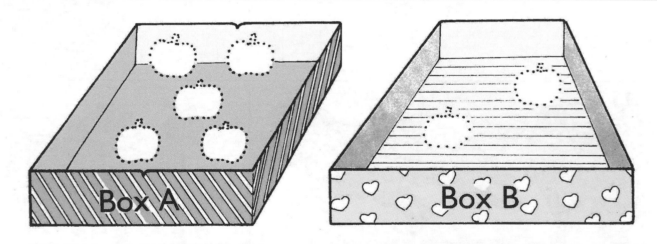

Box A contains _____ more apples than Box B.

# Draw matching lines. How many are left? Circle them and write the number.

Tom has ☐ hats.

Ali has ☐ hats.

Ali has _____ more hats than Tom.

Mary has ☐ books.

Ali has ☐ books.

Ali has _____ more books than Mary.

**Before using this page:** Ask a boy and a girl to stand in front of a class. Give the boy a bundle of 7 green rubber bands and the girl a bundle of 8 red rubber bands. Ask the class if they can tell how many each child has and who has more. Direct them to verify their answers by getting the two children to match their rubber bands one to one. Lead them to realize that to find the difference they have only to pair the objects in the two sets and count the unpaired objects.

**Using this page:** Let the children talk about the hats that Tom and Ali has. Ask them to draw one-to-one matching lines and circle the extra hat. Lead them to see that the 1 unmatched hat is the difference between the set of 5 and the set of 4. Ask them to write 1 in the blank. Continue the remaining exercises in the same fashion.

# Trace the pictures. Then fill in the missing numbers.

$$3 + 2 = \boxed{\phantom{0}}$$

$$7 - 3 = \boxed{\phantom{0}}$$

**Using this page:** Make up a number story for each picture, e.g. This is a carrot garden. Three rabbits are eating carrots. Then two more rabbits come to join them. Ask, "How many rabbits are there altogether? What is 3 + 2?" Direct them to write the answer in the box. For the second picture tell them that seven birds are resting on the fence. Three of them fly away. Ask, "How many birds are left? What is 7 – 3? Write the answer in the box".

# Trace the pictures. Then fill in the missing numbers.

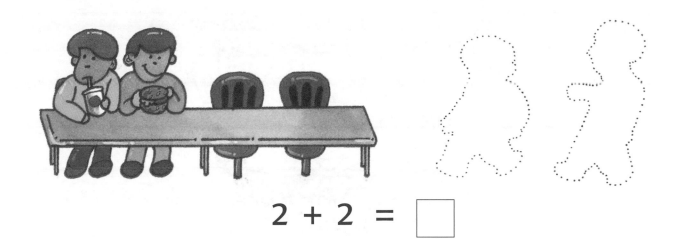

$$2 + 2 = \boxed{\phantom{0}}$$

$$4 - 1 = \boxed{\phantom{0}}$$

**Using this page:** Make up a number story for each picture, e.g. "Two boys are waiting for their friends to join them for lunch. At last their two friends have come". Make the children trace the two boys. Then ask, "How many boys are there altogether? What is 2 and 2? Write the answer in the boxes. For the second picture you may tell them that four children are playing on the swings. Suddenly one of them has a stomach ache so he quickly runs home. Then ask, "How many children were playing on the swings at first? How many children have gone home? What is 4 — 1? Write the answer in the box".

# Trace the pictures. Then fill in the missing numbers.

4 + 4 = ☐

8 − 3 = ☐

**Using this page:** Instruct the children to trace the balloons in the first picture. Ask, "How many balloons is the clown holding altogether? What happens to his balloons in the second picture? How many balloons does he have left?" Finally, have them write the answers in the boxes.

# Trace the 3 pigs. Then fill in the missing numbers.

$$1 + 1 + 1 = \boxed{\phantom{0}}$$

$$3 - 1 = \boxed{\phantom{0}}$$

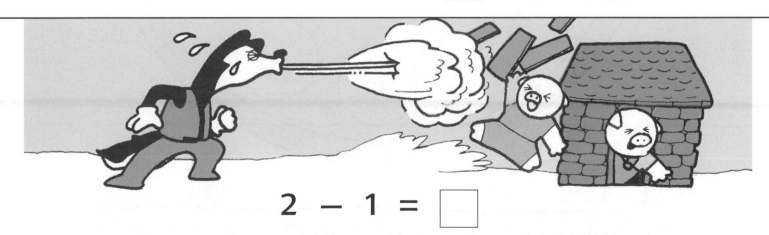

$$2 - 1 = \boxed{\phantom{0}}$$

**Before using this page:** Tell the children the story of the *Three Little Pigs*. Have them dramatize it. Direct the children to trace the three pigs.

**Using this page:** Discuss the first picture with the children. Ask questions that will lead them to say, "1 house is made of straw, 1 house is made of wood and 1 house is made of bricks. There are 3 houses altogether." In the same manner proceed to talk about the other two pictures and direct them to complete the number sentences.

# Fill in the missing numbers.
# Draw the hands of the clock.

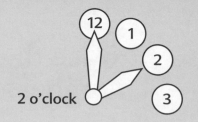

2 o'clock

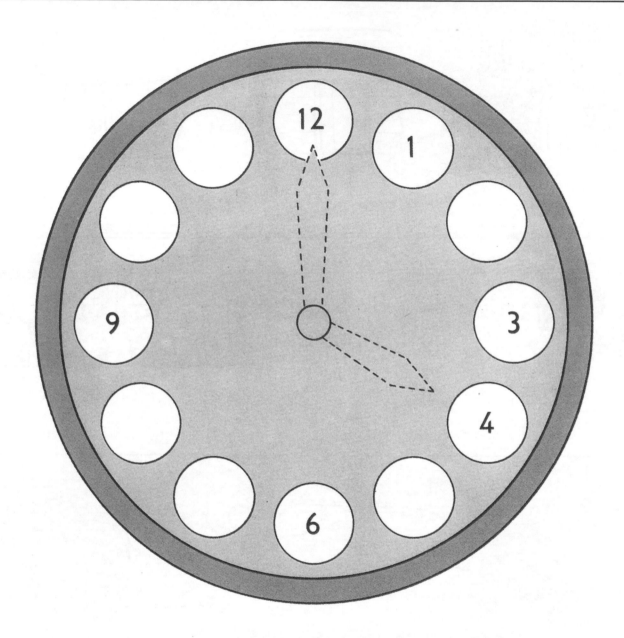

**Activity:** Hold up a clock and ask questions such as, "Are the two hands of the clock the same length? Do both hands move? Which hand moves faster, the long hand or the short hand?" Have the children read the numerals on the clock face and draw their attention to its clockwise direction. Ask them to show the direction with their fingers.

**Using this page:** Direct the children to fill in the missing numerals and trace the hands of the clock. Tell them that the long hand is called the **minute hand** and the short hand the **hour hand**. Ask, "At what number is the minute hand pointing? At what number is the hour hand pointing?" Tell the children that the **time** on this clock is 4 **o'clock**. Write it on the board.

# Write the time.

**1.**

☐ o'clock

**2.**

☐ o'clock

**3.**

☐ o'clock

**4.**

☐ o'clock

**5.**

☐ o'clock

**6.**

☐ o'clock

**Before using this page:** Discuss ways their schedule might change from day to day. Ask children whether they did the same thing at the same time yesterday or whether they will do the same thing at the same time tomorrow.

**Using this page:** Ask the children to look at each picture. Ask, "What is the boy in the first picture doing? What time does he wake up? Where is the minute hand? Where is the hour hand?" Ask similar questions for the rest of the pictures. Then direct the children to write the time in the boxes provided.

# Write the time.

☐ o'clock

☐ o'clock

☐ o'clock

**Activity:** Show 8 o'clock on a demonstration clock face. Ask the class to tell the time. Say, "It is 8 o'clock in the morning." Ask a volunteer to dramatize what he would be doing at this time of the day if it were a holiday. Then say, "Now it is 8 o'clock at night." Ask another volunteer to dramatize what he usually does at this time of the night. Continue the activity with other times of the day, e.g. 10 o'clock in the morning and 10 o'clock at night, 4 o'clock in the morning and 4 o'clock in the afternoon.

**Using this page:** Encourage the children to talk about what the girl is doing in each picture. Direct the children to write the numbers in the boxes provided.

46

# Write the time.

☐ o'clock

☐ o'clock

☐ o'clock

**Activity:** Display a demonstration clock face. Say, "The time is _____ o'clock."
Ask one child to move the clock hands to show the time stated. Repeat the
activity several times.
**Using this page:** Encourage the children to talk about what the boy is doing in
each picture and suggest what time of the day it is. Then ask them to write the
numbers in the boxes provided.

# Look and talk.

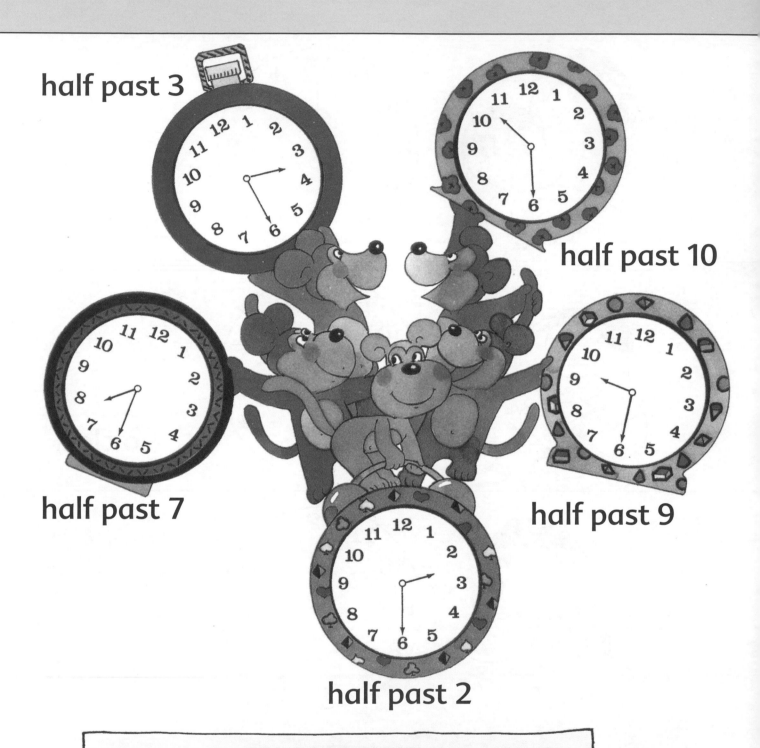

half past 3

half past 10

half past 7

half past 9

half past 2

**Activity:** Display a demonstration clock face. Set the clock at 4 o'clock. Tell the children that you are going to move the hands of the clock until it reads 5 o'clock. Explain that the long hand has moved all the way around the clock face and the short hand has moved from 4 to 5. Repeat the procedure, move the hands of the clock to stop at 4:30 and explain to them the long hand has moved half way around the clock face and the short hand is half-way between 4 and 5. Tell them the time shown on the clock is half-past 4. Demonstrate other half-hour times on the clock face.
**Using this page:** Ask the children to read the time shown on each clock face.

# Write the time.

half past 4

half past _____

half past _____

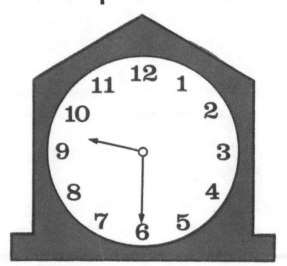

half past _____

half past _____

**Activity:** Show 2 o'clock on the demonstration clock and ask the children to read it. Explain that the minute hand begins at 12 and moves in a circle round the clock. Ask, "If I want to move the minute hand only **halfway round the clock**, where should I stop?" (At 6.) "Where will the hour hand be?" (Midway between 2 and 3.) Say, "This time is **half past** two." Write "half past 2" on the board. Using the demonstration clock, ask the children to tell the time as you set the clock at 4 o'clock, half past 4, 5 o'clock, half past 5, 6 o'clock, half past 6, and so on until the children can tell the time to the nearest half hour.
**Using this page:** Ask the children to look at each clock face, read the time given and fill in the missing numbers.

49

# Write the time.

half past _____

half past _____

half past _____

half past _____

half past _____

half past _____

half past _____

**Activity:** Give the children practice in reading times in hours and half hours using a demonstration clock.
**Using this page:** Have the children tell you the times orally. Then ask them to fill in the missing numbers.

# Write the time.

half past _____

_____ o'clock

o'clock

half past _____

half past _____

half past _____

**Activity:** Use a demonstration clock to give the children practice in reading times in hours and half hours.
**Using this page:** Discuss each picture and have the children read the time. Then ask them to fill in the numbers.

# Write the time.

half past _____

half past _____

half past _____

half past _____

half past _____

half past _____

**Activity:** Show half past 8 on the demonstration clock. Ask the children to state the positions of the minute hand and the hour hand. Next, call out other half hour times and ask individual volunteers to show the time on the demonstration clock.

**Using this page:** Direct the children to point to the first clock, describe the positions of the minute hand and hour hand, state the time and write the answer in the space provided. Allow those who can to work on the page independently.

# Write the days of the week.

first
Sunday

first

second

third

fourth

fifth

sixth

seventh

Saturday

Thursday

Friday

Wednesday

Tuesday

Monday

Sunday

**Activity and using this page:** Prepare a set of word cards on which are written the seven days of the week. Hold up the word card Sunday and have the children read it after you. Ask them to point to the word on this page and read it. Tell them that **Sunday** is the first day of the week. Discuss with them what they normally do on a Sunday. Then have them copy the word "Sunday" in the box labelled "first". Introduce the other days of the week in the same way. Show the children a calender. Tell them they will learn more about the calender later. Then ask them to find the names of the days of the week on it. Circle today on the calender and ask them what day of the week it is. Ask them what day of the week yesterday was and what day of the week tomorrow will be.

# Write the names of the days.

Friday

| Sunday | Monday | Tuesday |
| Wednesday | Thursday | Friday |
| | | Saturday |

Today

Tomorrow

Yesterday

**Before using this page:** Before they do the second exercise, ask, "What is the day today? What will you do after school today? What was the day yesterday? What fun things did you do yesterday? What day will tomorrow be? What are you planning to do tomorrow?" Direct them to write the name of each day in the boxes provided.

**Using this page:** Ask the children to identify and talk about the activities in each picture. Then ask them to match the small illustration to the larger one and write the name of the day on which this activity takes place in the box provided. Before they do the second exercise, ask, "What is the day today? What day will tomorrow be?" Direct them to write their answers in the boxes provided.

# Write the names of the days.

 Shopping on _____

 Picnic on _____

 Exercise on _____

 Swimming on _____

 Cycling on _____

 Party on _____

 Reading on _____

**Activity:** Ask one child to arrange the "Days of the Week" word cards on the ledge of the board in order. Ask another child to pick a word card, read it and tell the class what he/she did on that day last week. The child may dramatize the activity if he/she wishes.

**Using this page:** Ask the children to read the instructions with you. Look at the pictures and talk about what Wendy does on each day of the week. Then direct them to write the names of the days in the blanks provided.

# Write the names of the days.

| Sunday | Monday | Tuesday |
|--------|--------|---------|
| Wednesday | Thursday | Friday |
| | | Saturday |

cloudy day

_____

rainy days

_____  and  _____

sunny days

_____  and  _____

windy days

_____  and  _____

# Write the names of the days.

Sunday

Monday

Tuesday

Wednesday

Thursday

Friday

Saturday

Ben's birthday

Windy day

Camping

Rainy day

Going to school

Cloudy day

Sunny day

**Before using this page:** Ask the children to name the days of the week in order. Ask, "What day is it today? What day was yesterday? What day will tomorrow be? What day will it be in 2 days' time?" etc. Show the children a calender. Tell them that a calender shows all the days of the year. One row on the calender is one week. Count some or all of the rows. Tell the children that a year has 52 weeks. Discuss the highlights sequentially in a year such as holidays, seasons, start of school, birthdays. Find and point to some of those days on the calender and ask them what day of the week those days are. Ask them how old they are this year and how old they will be at their next birthday, either next year or later in the year. If some students know what day their birthday is, help them find that day on the calender.

**Using this page:** Talk about the pictures with the children. Read the phrases on this page with them. Direct them to complete the written work.

# Write the number.

| tens | ones |
|------|------|
| 2 | 0 |
| 20 | |

| tens | ones |
|------|------|
|      |      |

| tens | ones |
|------|------|
|      |      |

| tens | ones |
|------|------|
|      |      |

| tens | ones |
|------|------|
|      |      |

| tens | ones |
|------|------|
|      |      |

**Using pages 58 and 59:** Work through the exercises on these pages with the class. Ask the children to count and check that there are ten dots in each set. Then ask, "How many tens and ones are there in the first row?" Direct them to write 1 under the "tens" and 0 under the "ones". Ask, "What is another name for 1 ten and 0 ones?" Direct them to write 10 in the box. Guide them in the same way through the rest of the exercises. Finally, direct them to count the numbers in sequence: ten, twenty, thirty, ... one hundred.

# Write the number.

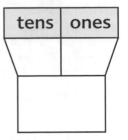

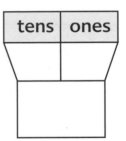

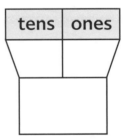

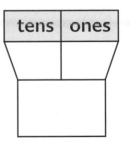

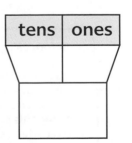

# Color the correct number.

10¢
10¢
10¢
20¢

| 10 | 20 | 30 | 40 | 50 |

| 10¢ | 10¢ | 10¢ | 10¢ | 10¢ |
| 10¢ | 10¢ | 10¢ | 10¢ | 10¢ |
| 10¢ | 10¢ | 10¢ | 10¢ | 10¢ |
| 10¢ | 10¢ | 10¢ | 10¢ | 10¢ |
| 10¢ | 10¢ | 10¢ | 10¢ | 10¢ |

| 10 | 20 | 30 | 40 | 50 |

**Before using this page:** Ask 5 children to stand in a row. Direct the first child to display his 10 fingers and get the class to say, "Ten". The second child displays his fingers together with the first child and the class counts twenty and so on up to fifty. Have the children count ten-cent coins like this: ten cents, twenty cents, thirty cents, forty cents, fifty cents.

**Using this page:** Ask the children to read the numerals in the first exercise. Next, direct them to read the numeral below each column of ten-cent coins and to color the correct number in each column.

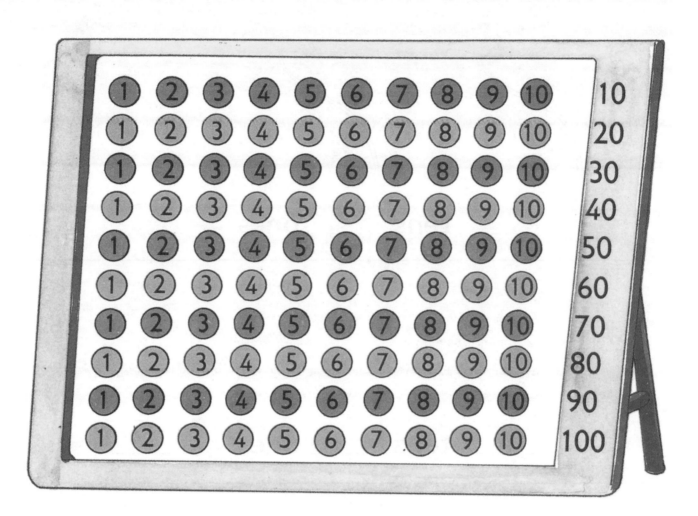

## Fill in the missing numbers.

| 10 | 20 |  | 40 | 50 |  | 70 |  | 90 |  |
|---|---|---|---|---|---|---|---|---|---|
| 10 |  |  | 40 |  | 60 |  |  |  | 100 |

**Using this page:** Talk about the number frame with the children. Direct them to count aloud in tens. Next, direct them to fill in the missing numerals in the second exercise.

# Trace the picture.
# Count and write.

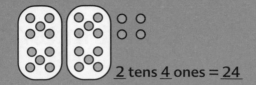

2 tens 4 ones = 24

_____ tens _____ ones = _____

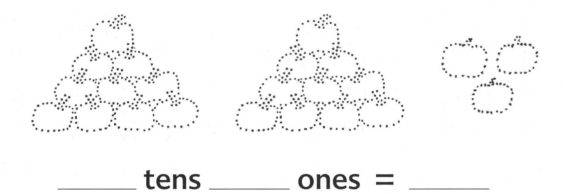

_____ tens _____ ones = _____

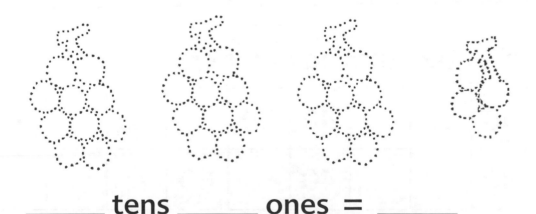

_____ tens _____ ones = _____

**Before using this page:** Put 100 counters in a bag. Ask a child to put in his hand and draw out as many counters as his hand can hold. Ask him to guess how many counters he has in his hand. Write down his guess. Then have him put them in groups of 10. Ask, "How many tens and ones are there?" Record his answers like this: \_\_\_\_ tens \_\_\_\_ ones = \_\_\_\_. Compare this answer with his estimate. Continue the activity with different individuals.
**Using this page:** Direct the children to count in sets of 10 and the remainder as loose ones. Then they record the answers as shown in the example.

# Circle sets of 10.
# Then count and write.

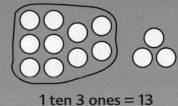

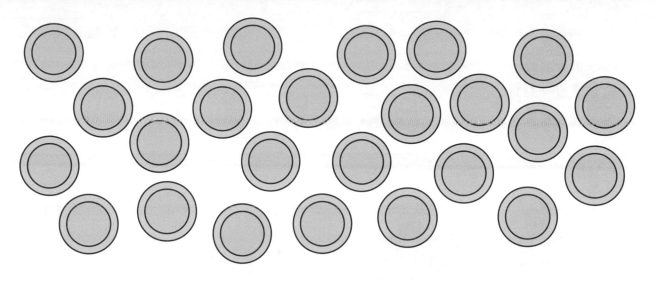

_____ tens _____ ones = _____

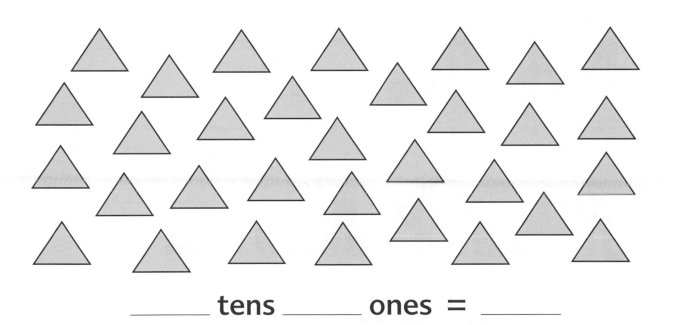

_____ tens _____ ones = _____

**Before using this page:** In advance, prepare a jar containing marbles or beans or other uniform small objects (less then 100). Ask the children to guess how many objects there are in the jar. Have an actual amount to the estimates. Repeat the activity with different individuals and different amounts.

**Using this page:** Ask the children to number the counters 1 to 10 and circle them. Repeat until there are no more sets of 10. Then they count the tens and ones and write the answers.

# Count and write.

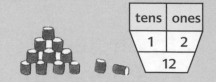

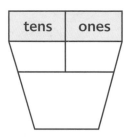

| tens | ones |
|------|------|
| | |

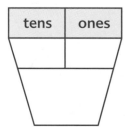

| tens | ones |
|------|------|
| | |

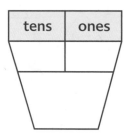

| tens | ones |
|------|------|
| | |

| tens | ones |
|------|------|
| | |

**Using this page:** Discuss the example given with the children. Do the first two exercises with the class to make sure they understand what is to be done. Then direct them to complete the remaining exercises on their own.

# Count and write.

**Before using this page:** Display sets of tens and single objects. Ask the children to tell you how many tens and ones there are and ask one child to say and write the corresponding numeral on the board.

**Using this page:** Work the first few exercises with the class. Count the spots on each group of mushrooms and write the numeral on each card. Then direct them to complete the exercises on their own.

# Fill in the missing numbers.
# Then read the numbers.

| 1 | 2 | 3 | 4 | 5 | 6 | | 8 | 9 | 10 |
|---|---|---|---|---|---|---|---|---|---|
| 11 | 12 | 13 | 14 | 15 | 16 | 17 | 18 | 19 | |
| 21 | 22 | 23 | 24 | 25 | 26 | 27 | 28 | 29 | 30 |
| 31 | 32 | 33 | 34 | 35 | 36 | 37 | 38 | 39 | 40 |
| 41 | 42 | 43 | 44 | 45 | 46 | 47 | 48 | 49 | 50 |
| 51 | 52 | 53 | 54 | 55 | 56 | 57 | | 59 | 60 |
| 61 | 62 | 63 | 64 | 65 | 66 | 67 | 68 | 69 | 70 |
| 71 | 72 | 73 | | 75 | 76 | 77 | 78 | 79 | 80 |
| 81 | | 83 | 84 | 85 | 86 | 87 | 88 | 89 | 90 |
| 91 | 92 | 93 | 94 | 95 | 96 | 97 | 98 | 99 | 100 |

**Using this page:** Direct the children to fill in the missing numerals. Then ask them to read out the numbers 1-100 together.

# Write the numbers in the boxes.

| | |
|---|---|
| | 5 |

Circle every fifth number.
Then read them.

| 1 | 2 | 3 | 4 | ⑤ | 6 | 7 | 8 | 9 | ⑩ |
|---|---|---|---|---|---|---|---|---|---|
| 11 | 12 | 13 | 14 | ⑮ | 16 | 17 | 18 | 19 | 20 |
| 21 | 22 | 23 | 24 | 25 | 26 | 27 | 28 | 29 | 30 |
| 31 | 32 | 33 | 34 | 35 | 36 | 37 | 38 | 39 | 40 |
| 41 | 42 | 43 | 44 | 45 | 46 | 47 | 48 | 49 | 50 |

**Before using this page:** Ask three children to stand in front of the classroom. Direct them to raise both their hands and ask the class to count their fingers. When they reach every fifth finger, ask one child to write the numeral on the board: 5, 10, 15, ...30. Next direct them to read the numerals on the board in sequence.
**Using this page:** Direct the children to count the fingers and write the numerals in the boxes. In the second exercise, direct them to circle every fifth box. When they have finished, ask them to read the circled numerals in sequence.

67

# Color every fifth stone.
# Write the numbers in the boxes.

**Using this page:** Talk about the picture with the children. Direct them to color every fifth stone and write the numeral in the signposts.

68

# Count in fives.
# Write the numbers in the boxes.

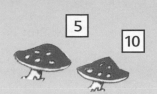

**Before using this page:** Using the numeral chart on page 67, review counting in fives up to 50 with the children.
**Using this page:** Tell the children that there are five spots on each mushroom. Direct them to count in fives and write the numerals in the boxes as they count: 5, 10, 15, ... 50.
**After using this page:** Ask the children to bring a set of coins consisting of a penny, a nickel, a dime and a quarter for the next day's lesson.

# Trace the coins.

25 cents

**penny**
**1 cent**

**nickel**
**5 cents**

**dime**
**10 cents**

**quarter**
**25 cents**

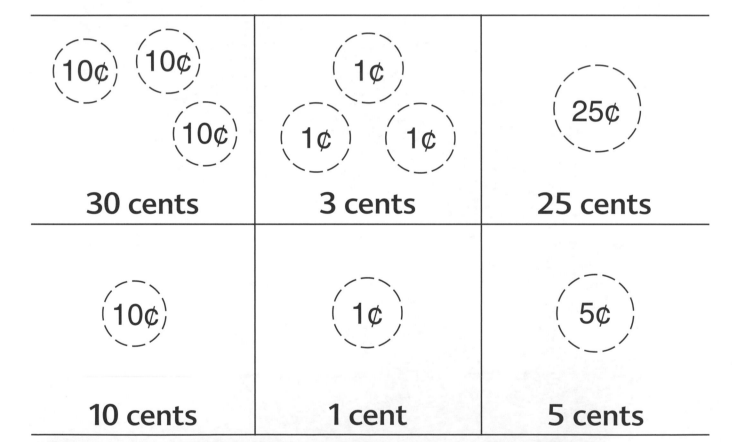

| 30 cents | 3 cents | 25 cents |
| 10 cents | 1 cent | 5 cents |

**Before using this page:** Ask the children to display on their tables the set of coins that you had asked them to bring the day before. Ask them to examine each coin carefully. Hold up a penny and say, "This is a 1-cent coin. It is called a penny. Show me your 1-cent coin. Introduce each of the other coins in the same way. Ask a student to pick up a penny and tell you its value. Continue with the other coins.

**Using this page:** Direct the children to match their coins with those illustrated on this page and make sure they look at both sides of each coin. Ask them to name the coins. Next, direct them to trace the coins in the boxes. Explain to them the symbol ¢ is the short form of cents. We read this ¢ as cents.

# Match the coin to the object.

25¢

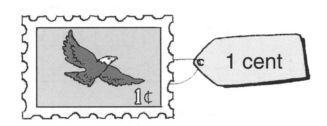

10¢

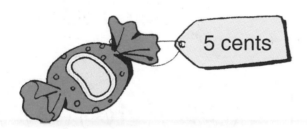

5¢

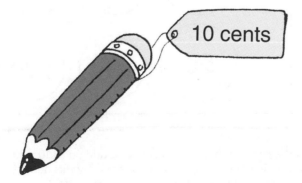

1¢

# Color the correct number of coins.

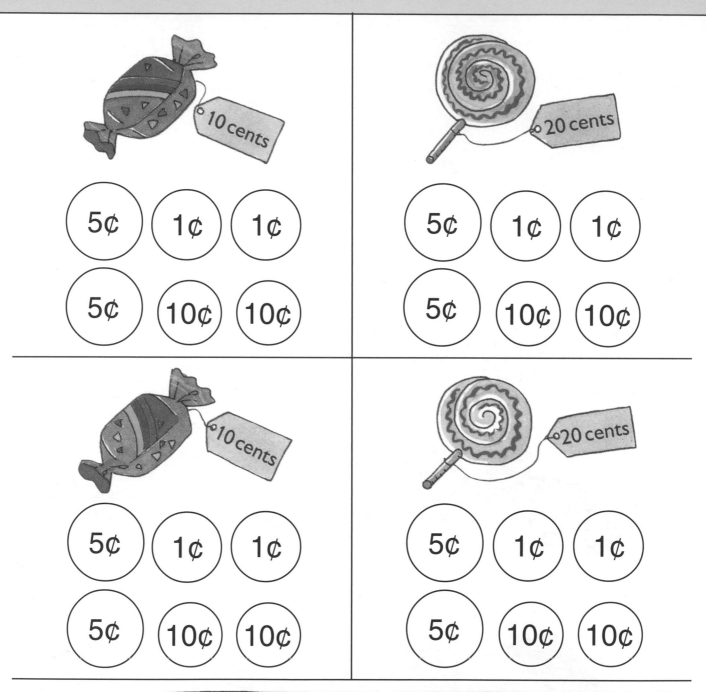

Before using this page: Show the children that two 5-cent coins add up to 10 cents, and that two 10-cent coins or four 5-cent coins add up to 20 cents. Try this activity: Hold up a dime and ask the children to suggest other ways to make up 10 cents, e.g. ten 1-cent coins or two 5-cent coins. Continue with this activity until the children understand the concept of the value of money.

Using this page: Direct the children to color the coin in the boxes according to the values shown. Note: Accept any combination of coins as long as they add up to the correct value.

25¢

## Draw a quarter.

20¢

## Draw two dimes.

20¢

## Draw four nickels.

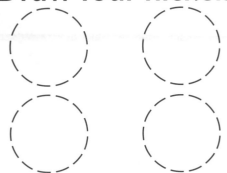

**Before using this page:** Review the name and value of each coin. Display an object with a price tag marked 25¢. Ask the children to tell you the price of the object. Display a collection of coins and ask individual children to select 1-cent coins, 5-cent coins, 10-cent coins and 25-cent coins to make up the value of the item.

**Using this page:** Direct the children to trace and fill in the value of each coin.

# Draw the correct number of coins.

## Draw 5-cent coins.

## Draw 5-cent coins.

## Draw 1-cent coins.

## Draw 1-cent coins.

**Before using this page:** Have the children take turns playing money changer. The money changer will probably need help from you in making his transactions, e.g. Three children give him a 25-cent play coin each. Each one needs different values of coins worth 25-cents. He must know that 25 one-cents, 5 five-cents or 2 ten-cents and 1 five-cent are worth a twenty-five cent coin.

**Using this page:** Ask the children to tell the value of each coin on this page. Then ask such questions as "How many five-cents are worth 25-cents? Finally ask them to draw each set of coins that make up the one given. For example in the first frame, they are to draw five 5-cent coins.

# Circle the correct number of coins.

Exercise BOOK NAME: ___

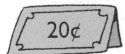 50¢

Joe

 40¢

Mrs. Lee

20¢

Mr. Ray

**Before using this page:** Review counting in tens and the value of money up to 50 cents.
**Using this page:** Talk about the objects and their prices by asking questions such as, "How much is the exercise book? How much money does Joe have? If he buys the exercise book, how much money will he have left?" Direct the children to circle the correct number of coins he will use to buy the exercise book. Proceed in the same way with the other two items.

75

# Circle the coins Jane spends.

60¢

| Jane buys | Jane spends |
|-----------|-------------|
| 30¢ | |
| 15¢ | |
| 40¢ | |

**Using this page:** Talk about the items and their prices with the children. Direct them to circle the correct number of coins needed to buy each item. Ask them which of the three items is the cheapest and which is the most expensive.
**After using this page:** Ask the children to bring a $1 bill for the next day's lesson.

# Circle the bills and coins Tom spends.

| Tom buys | Tom spends |
|---|---|
|  $ 2 |  |
|  $ 2.50 |  |

**Before using this page:** Ask the children to examine the $1 bill that you had instructed them to bring the day before. Next, hold up four quarters and ask such questions as "How many quarters make 1 dollar?"

**Using this page:** Discuss the example and money chart. Then talk about the prices of the objects that Tom buys and the bills and coins he needs to buy them. Then direct them to circle the bills and coins.

# Circle the fourth runner.

## Draw a line to join the word to the car.

| second | first | third |
|--------|-------|-------|

## Mark the longer one L and the short one S.

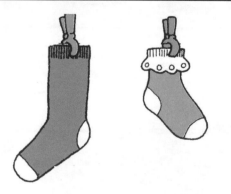

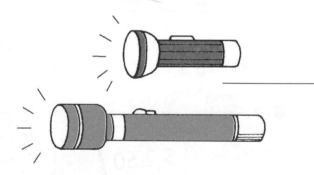

**Using this page:** Read the instructions to the children. Make sure they understand them. Then direct them to do the exercises on their own.

# Write the numbers in the boxes.

☐ **+** ☐ **=** ☐

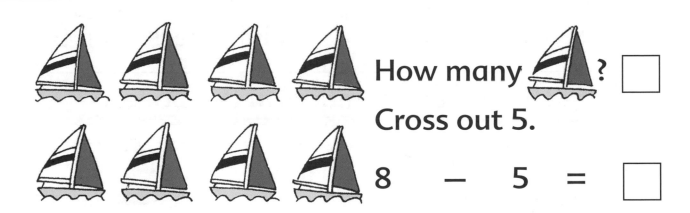

How many ? ☐

Cross out 5.

8 – 5 = ☐

Seven red apples
hanging on a tree.
Four fell off
And so there were ☐

**Before using this page:** Review addition and subtraction within 10.
**Using this page:** Discuss each group of exercises with the children. Explain to them what they have to do. Then direct them to complete the page on their own.

# Match and count.

 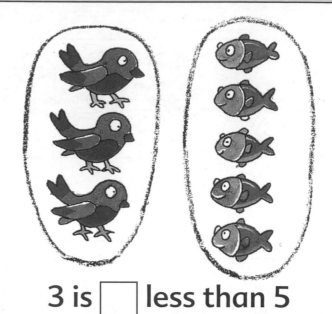

5 is ☐ more than 2

3 is ☐ less than 5

# Write the correct numbers in the boxes.

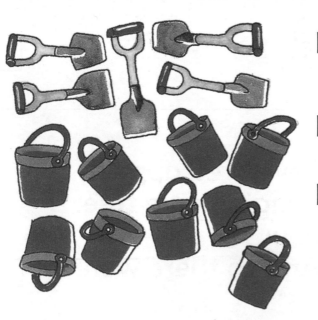

How many  ? ☐

How many  ? ☐

How many more

 than  ? ☐

**Using this page:** Direct the children to pair off the objects by drawing matching lines and to write the number of extra objects in the boxes provided. In the second exercise, it may be helpful for them to write the number 1 on a bucket and 1 on a shovel, 2 on a second bucket and 2 on a second shovel, and so on.